M000235751

# self-care

HERRON

# contents

# introduction

Hands up if you think self-care is a bubble bath and a girls' night out once in a while? It's often represented that way, but that's not it. In fact, self-care is kinda hard work. Or at least it's a curious combo of joy and discipline that takes work. It doesn't mean you can't visit a salt cave. You can if you like. But that's not the point. No, self-care plays the long game. Loving, valuing and nourishing ourselves in ways that help us travel in the direction we want to go in life: it's that kind of self-care. It's the self-care that says through constant, ongoing attention you can create a life you enjoy and from which you do not need to regularly escape.

Where to start? Understanding and embracing the self-care mindset is where it all begins: putting yourself first, setting boundaries, accepting and treating yourself with compassion. That stuff is a life's work so don't expect to nail it yesterday. But understanding its importance, putting it on your agenda and giving it your energy is a great place to start.

To live a self-care 'lifestyle', you'll need to prioritise the things that sustain us as human beings: good nutrition (and water), adequate sleep, exercise, positive relationships with others and activities or work that provide meaning and stability to your life. Put those things top of your to-do list.

After that, there are the things that help us live simply and efficiently, minimising the brain-drain that daily decisions and disorganisation can bring. Financial planning, meal planning, cleaning and visiting the dentist all qualify as self-care under that definition. And finding time to get them done with the minimum of fuss is important for looking after yourself.

In self-care, as in life, there is also space for pure pleasure. Indulge, escape, create, sing from the rooftops and dance among the wildflowers. Seek value and meaning in the long term, but make space for joy in your life today.

Self-care is here and now. It's the things that you do day in and day out. It's your routines and your habits. Sometimes it's little things that can be in done in under 15 minutes – waking up early, stretching, taking a breath, a short nap or a moment in the sun, walking the dog or writing a journal. When we do these things intentionally and mindfully, we practise self-care. And it's in the cumulative effect of practising them regularly that we see real benefits – the emergence of a calmer, happier, more caring and more cared-for you.

# the self-care mindset

'How we care for ourselves gives
our brain messages that shape our
self-worth so we must care for
ourselves in every way, every day.'

SAM OWEN

# consider what self-care means

Some people think that self-care is all about indulgence, but that's only a tiny part of it. It's great to treat yourself once in a while. All power to you. But true self-care – the act of caring for yourself – goes deeper. It requires you to wake up, take responsibility, look after yourself and create the life you want. To achieve this, you need to identify what matters to you and prioritise it relentlessly. And doing this may or may not be enjoyable in the short term. In the long term, however, it will create well-being.

'True self-care is not salt baths and chocolate cake, it is making the choice to build a life you don't need to regularly escape from.'

BRIANNA WIEST

♥

# know why self-care matters

Self-care matters. It helps prevent burnout, reduces the negative effects of stress, and helps us to focus on what is important in life. If you pay consistent and ongoing attention to your physical and emotional needs by sticking to your self-care routines, your mental health will benefit.

# understand its power

'Caring for myself is not self-indulgence, it is self-preservation and that is an act of political warfare.'

AUDRE LORDE

4

♥

# don't let guilt run the show

It's all too easy to feel guilty about self-care. For most of us, that's a big reason why it gets pushed to the bottom of the priority pile. We feel guilty because we perceive that self-care is selfish or indulgent. But nothing could be further from the truth. Self-care is hard and it requires you to be disciplined. Self-care equals self-respect. Respect yourself, then you'll take care of yourself. When you take care of yourself, you feel good about yourself. In that positive mindset, you will be better able to care well for others. So drop the guilt. By looking after yourself, you are looking after your family and future too.

'Guilt is a useless feeling. It's never enough to make you change direction - only enough to make you useless.'

DANIEL NAYERI

5

# be honest

'Being entirely honest with oneself is a good exercise.'

SIGMUND FREUD

# see yourself clearly

Being honest is hard. It requires you to uncover and accept the bits of yourself you've been trying to ignore. You need to put yourself out in the open. There's no room for living by comparison with others or seeking to meet impossible goals or standards. There's just you: your authentic self, who you really are. When you honestly know that person, then you can meet her needs. Certain people or patterns in your life may need to change as a result. But as these doors close, new ones open and behind them is your happiness.

# accept
# yourself

'Accept everything about yourself
– I mean everything, You are you and
that is the beginning and the end – no
apologies, no regrets.'

CLARK MOUSTAKAS

# take care
# of yourself

'Fall in love with taking care of yourself: mind, body, and soul. There is only one of you. You are truly once in a lifetime.'

LATISHA COTTO

# know your triggers

An emotional trigger is something that provokes upsetting feelings (and can lead to problematic behaviours too). To understand your triggers, tune in when you are feeling a familiar emotion, be that envy, sadness, anger or something else. What just happened to make you feel that way? Keep working on it, because there's a pattern and it's your job to uncover it. Remember that every single person on this planet has emotions and things that trigger them. But not everyone understands that we have the power to choose our responses. In our responses lie freedom from the habitual feelings that have held us back.

# learn coping strategies

'When we self-regulate well, we are better able to control the trajectory of our emotional lives and resulting actions based on our values and sense of purpose.'

AMY LEIGH MERCREE

# stand tall

'Self-care is an attitude that says
"I am responsible for myself."'

MELANIE BEATTIE

# eliminate negative self-talk

Start by listening to the voice inside your head. What is she saying? Take notes. Reflect and challenge. Is what she is saying objectively true? Whenever you hear this voice, pause. Catch your self-talk and replace it with a positive affirmation. Imagine what a loving parent might say to a child. Speak to yourself with that kind of generosity, forgiveness, positivity and love. Over time, this new voice will come to dominate your thoughts.

# be kind to yourself – always

'You are a human being and that is enough to warrant compassion and kindness.'

HANK GREEN

# be happy on your own

'Knowing how to be solitary is central to the art of loving. When we can be alone, we can be with others without using them as a means of escape.'

BELL HOOKS

# be disciplined

Step aside, facials and bubble baths. Enter, picking up the reins of your life and riding that horse. That means working out what your needs are and meeting them, day in, day out, today and each day. It's not about what feels good in the moment, but what will feel good in the long term. It is making the commitment to do what needs to be done in order to stay healthy and balanced. Perhaps its turning the TV off at night, making a family budget, ending a toxic relationship or building a new career. Self-care is whatever it takes to live your life authentically. And that takes time, hard work and discipline. Giddy up.

'We need to replace
your vicious stress
cycle with a vicious
cycle of self-care.'

DR. SARA GOTTFRIED

# check in with yourself

'Time spent in self-reflection is never wasted. It is an intimate date with yourself.'

PAUL T.P. WONG

'Check on yourself as much as you check on your Instagram.'

ANON

# give yourself a break

Next time you are giving yourself a hard time, try saying, 'Okay, I accept I did not do well here, but I have done x, y and z [insert things you are proud of]'. This simple trick provides an easy way to forgive yourself and move on. It liberates the mind from dwelling on 'the problem', freeing up vital mental resources that can now be put to better use.

# enjoy life

Identify what pleases you. Whether it's
certain people, places or activities. Focus
in on what they are and hold them dear.
Do more of them and less of the things
that don't make you happy. If you enjoy
life, you won't need to be constantly
thinking of ways to escape from it.

# put your oxygen mask on first

If you've ever been on an aeroplane you've heard the advice to put your own oxygen mask on first before helping others. If you're a parent, you've probably found that idea challenging. It goes against the grain to help yourself before helping your kids, surely? Ah, but if you can't breathe you can't save your children. Self-care? Same same.

# be on your side

'With every act of self-care, your authentic self gets stronger, and the critical, fearful mind gets weaker. Every act of self-care is a powerful declaration: I am on my side; I am on my side; each day I am more and more on my own side.'

SUSAN WEISS BERRY

21

♥

# go easy

'These mountains that you are carrying,
you were only supposed to climb.'

NAJWA ZEBIAN

# rethink your goals

Whether your goals are printed and laminated on your noticeboard or a loose collection of ideas in your head, you have got goals. We all have things we expect to happen or aspire to. Have a think about yours. Are they realistic and relevant? Realistic – can you actually achieve it? Relevant – on reflection, does it fit with who you (honestly) are? Ditch the goals that don't fit the 'realistic and relevant' criteria. Don't stress about giving up on goals. Look at it this way, giving up on some goals will create space for you to really care about the others.

♥

# set
# boundaries

'Love yourself enough to set boundaries. Your time and energy are precious. You get to choose how you use it. You teach people how to treat you by deciding what you will and won't accept.'

ANNA TAYLOR

# say 'no'

Chances are saying no is hard for you. That's true for most of us, as we try to meet the needs of others or appear accomplished. But learning to say no with confidence and certainty, on a regular basis, is a kind of superpower. (Picture yourself as Clark Kent if it helps.) When saying no, say no. Learn not to offer up excuses as an add-on. When people ask why, try honesty not excuses. If you are feeling overloaded and on the edge, say that. Chances are it will elicit greater sympathy than an excuse would. Saying no is a habit that you need to cultivate. Keep practising and the superpower will be yours.

♥

# say bye-bye to negative relationships

The world is full of wonderful people. You deserve friendship and love from those people. Creating positive relationships that will sustain you and bring joy is a fundamental act of self-care.

If you are currently holding on to relationships that don't serve you, let them go.

Unfollow, unfriend, delete, ignore.

'Don't let anyone rent a space in your head unless they're a good tenant.'

ANON

# find what works for YOU

There are lots of ideas in this book. Even more on a quick google of the term 'self-care'. And a tsunami of them on Instagram or Pinterest. The hard work of developing a self-care mindset – being compassionate towards ourselves, putting in time and effort towards self-care, and getting in touch with our authentic selves – those things are universal. But the 'what and how' is personal. It's important to remember this when it comes to self-care. It's whatever works for you. Don't try to do everything. Set your priorities based on your needs. Remember, 'one man's poison is another man's medicine'.

# make a choice

'Self-care is a deliberate choice to gift ourself with people, places, things, events, and opportunities that recharge our personal battery and promote whole health – body, mind, and spirit.'

LAURIE BUCHANAN

# schedule your self-care time

Design your schedule with your self-care plan in mind. Ensure that you are making time for the things that matter, whether that's the boring stuff like setting your weekly meal plan, or the things you enjoy like pursuing a hobby or socialising. Create the time and guard it with your life. If necessary, share this schedule with loved ones and encourage them to create their own.

# do something small

Try not to get overwhelmed. And let's be realistic, taking time for self-care is not always easy, but doing something small each day or week is a good start.

# the self-care lifestyle

'Self-care is how you
take your power back.'

LALAH DELIA

♥

# get enough sleep

Go to bed early (and around the same time each night). The zeds you knock out before midnight are worth double in their regenerative powers, maybe more, than those after.

The value of sleep simply cannot be underestimated. It builds physical and mental resilience, improves memory, sharpens attention and lowers stress.

If you are struggling with sleep, look into creating a night-time sleep ritual that works for you.

'It is a common experience that a problem difficult at night is resolved in the morning after the committee of sleep has worked on it.'

JOHN STEINBECK

# drink water

Your body is always showing up for you, doing its best to support you and help you enjoy life. Now it's your turn to show up for your body. Water. It needs water to survive. Every cell, tissue and organ in your body needs water to work properly. Water helps regulate your body temperature, lubricate joints, eliminate nasties from the body and boost the immune system.

So fill up your water bottle. And drink.

'Don't forget to drink water and get some sun. You're basically a house plant with more complicated emotions.'

ANON

# eat well

Like sleep, nutrition is a foundation stone of self-care. Eating well boosts both your physical and mental health. You know the rules: eat the rainbow (all the colours of fruit and vegetables), shop the aisles at the supermarket where the fresh produce lives, watch your portion sizes, don't eat in front of the TV, eat less sugar and more good fats. You got that? Good, because like drinking water, eating well is a simple but radical act of self-care. High five.

# take care of your gut

People are talking about gut health. Boy, are they talking. The gut has even been called the second brain. This idea has taken the wellness world by storm and traditional medics are not far behind. Hype aside, fact is that the gut is home to 90 per cent of your body's serotonin – the nifty little neurotransmitter that helps control your mood, sleep and appetite. The gut also acts as a barrier, keeping harmful bacteria out and good bacteria in. When this barrier gets inflamed (called leaky gut) it can wreak all kinds of havoc on your health. Including gut-friendly foods such as yoghurt and almonds in your daily diet is a good place to start taking care of your gut.

# use your sick days

What's the deal with accumulating sick days? If you've got a specific goal for using them in mind, then sure. But if you're trying to impress the boss, put the polish on your HR file or engage in some compulsive hoarding activity then hey, stop it, you. You don't need another hero. You don't have to be on death's door to take a sick day. And a mental-health day is a sick day too. If you need, it take it.

And don't spend the day feeling guilty about it.

# take a lunch break

It's tricky trying to single-finger-type an important email clutching onto a limp ham sandwich, isn't it? But more than half of us attempt the lunch-at-desk feat daily. We are simply too busy, too important or our position at work is too vulnerable for us to go outside, soak up some sunshine, talk to a friend, read a book in the park and have the break from work that the lunch hour was intended for. Here's the thing. It's been proven that taking a break increases our productivity. When you went, nobody thought anything of it. And if your job is really so vulnerable, it's probably not the best job for you. So take a lunch break.

# count your steps

'If I get bored while walking, I count my steps to know how many impressions I left today.'

ANON

# walk the dog

If you don't have a dog, you could offer to walk someone else's. Or just go for a walk anyway. The World Health Organization recommends that adults 18 to 65 years old engage in moderate exercise for 30 minutes five days a week and in strengthening exercises twice weekly. Dogs provide great motivation, but there are other ways to get motivated. Walk with a friend or walking group. Or use technology as your friend in this case. There are some excellent activity-tracking apps out there. If you're a numbers kind of person, you can count your steps (10,000 a day is the goal) or work towards whatever goals you set.

# honour your body

Ours is a world dominated by rules about our bodies – how they should look, what they should weigh – and endless invitations to change them through beautification, clothing or even surgery. We cannot turn our heads without the opportunity to compare ourselves to others and find ourselves lacking. Is it any wonder that we forget to honour our bodies? For their constancy. For rising above our ill thoughts. They are here for us always, home to our souls and our senses. They sustain us and bring us pleasure. Treat your body – your physical self – with care.

'I spoke to my body and asked it to be my friend. It took a breath, and responded "I have been waiting patiently for you."'

ANON

# exercise

Go on a bike ride, go for a run, go to the gym, join a tennis club, take a yoga class, play a team sports, go for a walk before or after work. The options are limitless and it's whatever floats your boat. The trick though is to do it. Because exercise will make you feel good (thanks, endorphins), give you energy for the day, help you think more clearly and sleep better. Plus, it's time that's just for you.

It's never too late to start and you're never too unfit to exercise. It takes 21 days to make a routine, so find something you enjoy and commit to doing it for that long.

# go to the dentist

It might not be top of most people's self-care lists, but a visit to the dentist (or other health professional) is self-care. In the juggle of family and work life, listening to our bodies and taking care of them is often deprioritised. Whether it's fixing a health problem, giving you peace of mind or preventing a problem in the future, paying attention to your medical needs is important.

# meditate

Buddhists claim meditation transforms the mind. Scientists have proven it. Studies have shown it decreases activity in the part of the brain commonly known as the 'monkey mind', as well as cell volume in the amygdala, brain-central for anxiety, stress and fear. At the same time it increases activity in the hippocampus, responsible for learning, memory and emotional regulation. Meditation has no rival when it comes to gaining clarity of mind, calmness and insight. The practice of meditation focusses on stillness and the breath. This can be done in silence or with the use of guided mediations found on YouTube or in apps.

'Deep breaths are like little love notes to your body.'

KELLIE RAE ROBERTS

# eliminate decisions

It's estimated that we make about 35,000 remotely conscious decisions a day. That's a heavy load on the brain. Free up some space by creating easy habits you can do automatically, such as locking in your exercise routine, checking email twice a day or planning meals ahead.

# don't rush

'Rushing never saved the time that planning did.'

BEN PARRIS

♥

# plan your week

Something seemingly small, like keeping a weekly planner on the fridge, can be helpful. On it you can write down all your responsibilities and appointments, helping you see at a glance what needs to be done each day.

'There cannot be a stressful crisis next week. My schedule is already full.'

HENRY KISSINGER

# prepare a cleaning schedule

Everybody's gotta do cleaning. It's a boring fact of life. On the self-care scale the act of cleaning scores high on discipline and low on joy for most of us. But the output – a clean and tidy environment – scores highly, so the key is to make getting it done as easy and efficient as possible. A master cleaning schedule provides structure, enabling you to do a daily whip around to stay on top of things, while also designating specific days and times to get bigger jobs done. Download a cleaning schedule from the internet, or make your own. Stick it on the fridge and make it happen. #selfcarewin

# create a master grocery list

Why is that whenever you go to write your grocery list, all the things you know you needed disappear from your mind? Trying to remember them is a drain on the brain. Enter master grocery lists, which contain a complete list of all the foods and household necessities you use. Refer to it each time you prepare your shopping list, cross referencing with your weekly meal plan and what you have in the pantry, fridge or freezer. You can go old school, by writing in a notebook, or download a template online. Or try an app such as AnyList, which allows you to link to recipes, work to a budget, store grocery lists and share this with your partner. #almostfun

# never lose your keys again

'A place for everything and everything in its place' is the organising mantra familiar to most of us. To make it happen, first be ruthless about purging so that you don't waste time organising things you don't need. Next, determine where items are going to live. Reorganise your space as needed to accommodate this. You'll need containers of the right shape and size, and labels so that you can locate what you want easily. This system will only work with co-operation from others, and with maintenance. But then, hey presto. You'll never be fumbling in your pockets or handbag for your keys again.

# look out for future you

Financial self-care. It's a thing. And it's not the $100 a month you set aside for your gym membership. No, it's creating a firm financial foundation for your life. Just as you look out for your emotional and physical health, financial well-being is key to your self-care plan. If you're stuck where to start, try just talking about money – with your partner, friends or financial specialists. Get the conversation started and you'll bring energy and focus to the topic. Set financial goals, tackle debt with an action plan and build a budget. Reframe the agenda so that instead of money having control over you, you have control over it.

# spend
# intentionally

The opportunity to spend is everywhere.
Not just on the high street, but at the
click of a button. The pressure to keep
up with the Joneses is fuelled by what we
see on social media. Consumerism, it's
easy and it's everywhere. But impulsive
spending often brings remorse and
shame. Whereas intentional spending
focusses on things that bring value and
fulfilment. At the very least, stop and
think before you buy. Ask yourself 'Is this
purchase bringing me value, is it within
my budget and do I need it?'

# budget

Create a budget and check in with your progress regularly (weekly would be good). There are plenty of easy-to-use and effective budgeting tools online. Aim to live within your means and eventually to eliminate debt from your life. It's not sexy, but it can provide you with freedom – to make different life choices and to live a life unencumbered by constant stress about money.

# find your motivation

Dragging yourself into work each day because you hate your job is draining. We can't all have an amazing, interesting and well-paid job that chimes perfectly with our identity. But we can find work that matters to us because we do it for a reason that matters to us. That reason might be financial security, creative fulfilment, intellectual stimulation, helping others or flexing a moral muscle. If you understand why you are doing something, it makes it easier to find the motivation to keep doing it, even on bad days.

# keep learning

Whatever your position, you can keep learning and growing professionally. Read journals, join online networking groups, take professional-development courses. It is important to keep pace with changes and stay engaged with your chosen career.

# take a victory lap

Whether you work from home or within a company, keep a focus on your achievements and don't let them pass without proper celebration. It's easy to be so busy that we immediately rush onto the next project. Instead make a note (actually write it down) of your successes and the things you enjoyed. This will give you a boost and make you feel more positive.

# set work-life boundaries

If you work from home you are not alone.
The benefits are well known, but there
are downsides too, including a sense
of never being able to get away from it.
Set yourself up well to work from home.
Get a nice desk and comfortable chair
both optimised for work. Put up quotes,
artwork or images that inspire you or
remind you of the people and things
that matter. Have your breakfast and get
dressed before you start work. Answer
emails at set times daily, not constantly.
Shut down your email at the end of your
working day and do something symbolic,
like going for a walk, to switch gears into
your personal time.

# read a story

When you find yourself distracted or endlessly scrolling, try picking up a book instead. Reading has benefits akin to meditation, allowing us to become totally absorbed, calm and relaxed. A study has shown that within six minutes of starting reading, the heart rate slows and muscle tension eases by more than 65 per cent. Regular readers sleep better, are less stressed, feel better about themselves and are less depressed in general. Reading stories in particular has added benefits such as helping develop empathy. Getting into the head of a character creates understanding. And stories open our minds, as we learn to see things from the point of view of others.

# take a nap

There's still a stigma associated with napping. Isn't it just for the very young and the very old? In fact, most species operate on a kind of napping schedule, whereas we humans have decided to divide our days into two periods: sleep and wake. (Perhaps so we could fit in all that work in between.) Regardless, napping has been scientifically proven to improve mood and performance and reduce fatigue. Don't do it too late in the day though, as night-time sleep is still the holy grail. Also some people just can't shake off the grumbles after they wake from a nap. If so, napping might not be your thing. Try it. And if it works for you, let yourself take a nap once in a while.

# aim to do what you love

It's easy to say 'Follow your passion and everything will fall into place' but for most people that's not very realistic. We might not have a single passion (most people don't) and even if we do, we still have a mortgage to pay. But we can all work towards doing what we love. If we feel that it is within our control, that it is possible and that we deserve it then that's more than half the battle. Combine this positive mindset with hard work, self-belief and a flexible approach, and anything is possible.

# be the light

'By doing what you love you inspire and awaken the hearts of others.'

SATSUKI SHIBUYA

# learn something new

Learning is good for your brain. New neural pathways form and electrical impulses shoot faster along them as you process new information. Learning helps build confidence and can provide an environment in which to meet others, helping satisfy our human need for connection. Plus, learning stimulates creativity as new information and new perspectives help us join the dots in new ways. Whether it's a sport, musical instrument, craft activity or something heady like writing or blogging, learning a new skill is good for you.

'We can learn something new anytime we believe we can...'

VIRGINIA SATIR

# be absorbed

Take time out to do something that you
can become completely absorbed in. This
might be a puzzle or adult colouring-in
book, perhaps a DIY project or even a
'chore' such as sharpening the kitchen
knives. An activity like this provides a good
way to take time out and by doing it you
may even enter what psychologists call
'flow' (more commonly known as 'being
in the zone'), which is when we become
so immersed in what we're doing that we
temporarily lose touch with time and even
our own existence. In a good way.

# don't give a damn

To practise the art of not giving a s**t, which is a fundamental skill to have in your self-care toolkit, experiment with doing something creative such as a painting or a piece of writing and not caring whether it's good or not. You can chuck it right in the bin if you like. Who cares? Keep on practising until you feel your inner judge-on-high-of-all-that-is-perfect just slip-slidin' away.

# turn your bathroom into a spa

Sometimes you just need to run a bubble bath, light a scented candle and shut the bathroom door on the world. Go the extra mile and put on face mask or other body treatment if you feel like it. Make sure you have spa-worthy, clean, fluffy towels, and nice slippers and a robe to put on afterwards. And, relax. #costsnothing

# dress up

How you look shouldn't matter and it
doesn't really, but let's face it, sometimes
it makes you feel simply invincible to
do your hair and make-up, put on your
favourite or most glamorous clothes and
look the world right the eye. If you feel
that way, do it. You don't need a reason.

♥

# do some gardening

'Flowers are restful to look at.
They have no emotions or conflict.'

SIGMUND FREUD

# indulge

Self-care is not self-indulgence but you can still indulge when the fancy takes you. Everybody deserves a treat, so what's yours? Some people love a luxury spa treatment or beauty therapy. Salt caves (or salt therapy) are popular too and are thought to have all sorts of health benefits. Or perhaps you'd prefer to go for a walk on the beach or out for a delicious meal. Whatever you like to do, do it from time to time for no other reason than that you want to and you enjoy it.

# organise a social event

Whether it's a girls' (or boys') night out or a hike with a friend, staying connected with others is a key pillar of self-care. Like food, water and exercise, emotional connection is fundamental to human survival.

# have an adult sleepover

Here's a curious thing. When out-of-town friends visit, it's perfectly acceptable to have a 'sleepover'. It's a joy to catch up late into the night and extend the conversation over coffee and pancakes in the morning. Our cups are replenished. But unless we have visitors, we don't consider doing it. Why not organise a sleepover with your friend? Enjoy taking time out of your routine, placing value on your friendship and doing things differently. Don't forget your toothbrush.

# make time for each other

As we race through life in a flurry of kids, work, sports and essential appointments, it's easy to forget about the one we love the most. Sometimes we might even forget why we love them the most. But it's a flame that's usually easy to reignite. Make plans: a surprise date, a regular date, any kind of date. If getting out of the house is too hard, even a date at home would work (think candlelit dinner). A good relationship with a partner is second only to a good relationship with yourself. Don't neglect it.

'All relationships
have one law.
Never make the one
you love feel alone,
especially when
you're there.'

ANON

# get out in nature

The awesome power of Mother Nature cannot be underestimated. Even looking at a lovely view has been scientifically proven to reduce stress and help patients combat physical pain. Without really understanding why, scientists have also found that being in nature improves our mood and overall well-being, providing a renewed sense of purpose and vitality. Time spent in nature connects us to each other and to the world.

'To walk in nature
is to witness a
thousand miracles.'

MARY DAVIS

# go for a swim

'Live in the sunshine.
Swim in the sea.
Drink the wild air.'

RALPH WALDO EMERSON

# learn to surf

Surfing is the sweet spot. A spiritual sport if ever there was one, in which participants get to combine heart-pumping exercise with nature's most prized gift, the ocean, and the camaraderie that comes from a shared passion. It's even been proven to reduce post-traumatic stress in war veterans.

# visit an art gallery

You don't have to be an artist or knowledgeable about art to enjoy visiting a gallery. These calm, beautiful spaces are usually free to enter (bonus) and provide a tranquil environment in which to potter, ponder, sit and wonder. It can be a meditative experience. And then there's the art. It might inspire you. It might provoke you. It will probably make you think or feel something. It might spur a creative idea. At the very least, art galleries provide us with perspective and remind us that we are part of something much larger than ourselves.

# go to the library

'People may go to the library looking mainly for information, but they find each other there.'

ROBERT PUTNAM

# host a self-care party

Get your self-care crew on board. Be clear that this time together is intentional. You and your friends have taken time out to focus together on self-care. As well as the usual party frou frou and catering, consider designing self-care activities to do together. For example, each person writes down something that they want to do for their self-care but don't have time for. Then brainstorm solutions to the problem as a group. Give everyone a turn. Or write down and share affirmations or gratitude lists. You can use email or party planning tools to design the party agenda together as a group.

# help others

'Rest and self-care are so important.
When you take time to replenish your
spirit, it allows you to serve others from
the overflow. You cannot serve from an
empty vessel.'

ELEANOR BROWNN

# wear your pyjamas all day

'Sometimes self-care is exercise and eating right. Sometimes it's spending time with loved ones or taking a nap. And sometimes it's watching an entire season of television in one weekend while you lounge around in your pajamas. Whatever soothes your soul.'

NANEA HOFFMAN

# have a staycation

When is a holiday not a holiday? When you spend more time organising, packing and worrying than you do relaxing. Solution: staycation. That's a holiday spent at home. This will serve you up almost 100 per cent restful time with little or no prep required. See it as an opportunity to view the same thing with fresh eyes. You could try going to your usual place, but with a different person, at a different time or to do something different. Read a book at a cafe or have a picnic in your local park. Book yourself an activity day, and explore something new in your area. Or do something you regularly do as a family – but by yourself.

# go somewhere new

'Broad, wholesome, charitable views of men and things cannot be acquired by vegetating in one little corner of the earth all one's lifetime.'

MARK TWAIN

# get lost

It's kinda hard to get lost these days, with Google and other apps on standby ready to whisk us to our destination in the most direct way possible. But diversions are nice, often providing us with something new to experience. Getting lost can be a journey in itself. Academics have suggested that getting lost – whether that's literally lost or mentally lost in a question – is essential to our growth as people. In dispensing with Google maps, for instance, we force our brains to use higher reasoning and intuition to find a solution and so we find a way to find our way.

# self-care in 15 minutes or less

'Great things are done by a
series of small things done together.'

VINCENT VAN GOGH

# wake up refreshed

Before you go to bed, leave a glass of water on your bedside table and drink it after waking up. It will help to get you going.

# wake up early

'The time just before dawn contains the most energy of all hours of the day. This has helped me become an early riser and an early doer... When I wake to see that it's light out already, I feel the world has started without me.'

TERRI GUILLEMETS

# meditate for five minutes

You can meditate whenever you like, or get a chance, but research suggests that first thing in the morning is the ideal time. Its benefits are maximised when the mind is clear, free from the stresses of the day. You can meditate for however long you like, but five minutes is fine and a great start. Build up from there if you want to. Why bother? It will help to set you up for the day, generating an overall sense of calm and well-being, and enable you to tackle the day with greater focus and energy.

'Slow down.
Calm down.
Don't worry.
Don't hurry.
Trust the process.'

ALEXANDRA STODDARD

# watch the sunrise

'Rest but never quit. Even the sun has a sinking spell each evening. But it always rises the next morning. At sunrise, every soul is born again.'

MUHAMMAD ALI

# take a moment for your mantra

Set your intention for the day by repeating your chosen mantra (google it if you can't think of one.) Bond with your mantra and make it your own. You can chant it, speak it out loud in front of the mirror or write it down.

# drink your coffee

Choose your favourite mug. Notice where in the world the coffee grains have come from. Observe the smell and the noise as your coffee brews. Fill the mug and pick it up, noting its warmth. Take a sip. Savour its smell and rich, earthy flavour. Notice the sensation in your mouth. Slowly but surely begin to tune into your day. That's right: drink your coffee mindfully.

# stretch

Like food, water and the air we breathe, stretching is good. It keeps your muscles flexible, strong and healthy. It helps your blood flow and calms the mind. You can do it before you even get out of bed in the morning. Or set yourself a simple five-minute stretching routine to do while the sun rises. It's a wonderful way to start your day. If you work at an office, stop and stretch. If you don't work at an office, stop and stretch. You get the picture.

# put your legs up in the air

It's known in yoga as Viparita Karani (or Legs Up the Wall Pose). And it's got to be the pose that delivers the biggest bang for your stretchy buck. It's easy. It doesn't hurt. It only takes 15 minutes at most (and less is fine). And it's soooo good for you. It calms the nervous system, quietens the mind, relieves tired legs and feet, and eases back pain. Find a time to do it daily and reap the rewards. Set a reminder on your phone if it helps.

# do a burst of exercise

Do something fun (or silly) to get your heart racing. Run up and down the stairs, chase the kids round the garden, do a crazy dance. Just a few minutes at a time done regularly can radically improve your health. See if you can make your short bursts add up to 20 minutes a day and you'll be kicking some serious healthcare (equals self-care) goals.

♥

# sing at the top of your lungs

'The only thing better than singing is more singing.'

ELLA FITZGERALD

# create a positive playlist

'Music is probably the only real magic I have encountered in my life. There's not some trick involved with it. It's pure and it's real. It moves, it heals, it communicates and does all these incredible things.'

TOM PETTY

# get inspired

What inspires you? Is it motivational quotes, pictures of tropical islands, photos of family or images of amazing homes? Work out what it is and then find a way to keep your inspiration top of mind. Maybe it's by creating a vision board (or Pinterest board) or by writing down ideas or quotes and placing them somewhere prominent.

# set a daily event

Love a funny cat or cute baby video, or is a hit of hard news more your style? Whatever it is that you enjoy, rather than defaulting to it whenever you feel your mind wandering from its task, set a recurring daily event in your calendar. Ten minutes should do the trick. Then go cat-video-crazy.

♥

# keep a journal

'[Journaling] is like whispering to one's self and listening at the same time.'

MINA MURRAY

# use journaling prompts

Keeping a daily journal of your thoughts, what worries you and what inspires you, is one of the best productivity tools there is. But if you find yourself staring at a blank page, try journaling prompts. These are targeted questions can help you start writing when you're stuck for inspiration. Often it's only a little push we need to get going.

# practise gratitude

Gratitude is strongly associated with increased levels of happiness. Start practising it today by writing a gratitude list. It doesn't need to be exhaustive – start with five or 10 things.

Sometimes it might feel that gratitude flows from the pen, but other days it will be hard to summon anything much to be thankful for. If that happens, be grateful to yourself for even trying.

# create an a-z of me

Make it funny, make it deep, make it unflinchingly honest. It's up to you. But here's an interesting spin on the 'write down what I like about myself' idea. Create an alphabet of words about you – it could be words to describe yourself (A is for active) or foods you like to eat (B is for blueberries) or hobbies you enjoy (M is for macrame) or used to enjoy as a kid (J is for jazz ballet).

# start a mood tracker

Emotional self-regulation is important to self-care, but it can be hard to pinpoint our feelings if we don't pay careful attention. Plus, most of us ride the roller coaster of emotions rather than stop, pause and think about what's going on. Using a mood tracker can help. It's helpful to see our emotions represented visually and empowering to see changes, and how far we've come over time. Whether it's custom made, store bought, or an app, a mood tracker is a tool that can help you take care of yourself and make improvements to your daily life.

# start a feel-good file

Whether you choose to make a document on your desktop or just an old-school folder, the idea is to create a place where you can collect happy memories, photos, complements you have received, great experiences, hopes, wishes and dreams. Have a look through it when you need a boost or a bit of inspiration.

# give to others

A growing body of research shows that giving to others has a positive impact on your physical and mental health. It could be a gift, a donation to charity or a random act of kindness such as paying for someone's coffee or meal.

'We make a living by
what we get.
We make a life by
what we give.'

WINSTON CHURCHILL

# make a cup of tea

'If you are cold, tea will warm you; if you are too heated, it will cool you; if you are depressed, it will cheer you; if you are excited, it will calm you.'

WILLIAM EWART GLADSTONE

# have a think

Find a new podcast to listen to, read an interesting article that makes you think and provides you with a fresh, different perspective. Pick up a book. Whenever you read something that resonates, write the insight down so you don't forget.

# sign up to a community event

It takes just a couple of minutes to pick up the phone or send an email and say 'Yes' to getting involved in an event in your community. It might be helping out at the school or an organisation you already belong to. Or maybe it's something completely new that caught your eye in the local paper. Getting involved in the community where we live improves our sense of belonging, helps us to build meaningful relationships with neighbours and can provide purpose and meaning to our lives.

'We cannot live
only for ourselves.
A thousand fibers
connect us with our
fellow men.'

HERMAN MELVILLE

# care for your plants

Houseplants are so on trend right now. They look amazing and they are good for your health. They do the opposite of what we do when we breathe – they release oxygen and absorb carbon dioxide, freshening the air and eliminating nasty toxins. Taking the time to select and look after your houseplants is a simple, beautiful act of self-care.

# pick some lavender

If you are lucky enough to have lavender growing in your garden (and if you don't, plant some – it's easy to grow), then harvesting it and putting it to good use is therapeutic. After the lavender has dried (this takes about a week) you can use it to cook with (think lavender syrup or buttercream), to make bath salts, to make lavender bath bombs or wands (google it – a great project to do with the kids), as a drawer-deodoriser or simply as a decoration in the home. Lavender is so versatile and its earthy, pungent smell is invigorating.

# send a love note

Write a love note and mail it to your other half. Or put it in his wallet or lunchbox.
#awww

# share the love

'Tell someone you love them today, because life is short. But shout it at them in German because life is also terrifying and confusing.'

ANON

# speak nicely to yourself

Look yourself in the mirror and say 'I love you' or leave yourself a note to that effect. You could also consider saying more specific affirmations to yourself, such as 'I am strong', 'I am enough' or whatever it is that you need to hear. Even if it feels a bit embarrassing, try sticking with it. Just as eliminating negative self-talk is important, finding a voice and words with which to speak nicely to ourselves is too.

'The words you speak
become the house
on live in.'

HAFIZ

# call an
# old friend

Call someone you've lost touch with for
no real reason, or someone you haven't
spoken to in a while. Sometimes it's hard
to do, but it always feels great.

# make plans with someone

It's nice to have social events to look forward to in the calendar. If your calendar is a bit too empty for your liking, then make some plans. You could invite your co-workers out for lunch or a drink, plan an adventure with a good friend or a romantic date with your other half.

# create a bucket list

Bucket lists are cool because they make us stop and think what we actually want to experience in our time on planet Earth. They remind us that this time is short and to make the most of it we need to be proactive. Here's how to do it. Set aside 15 minutes and grab a piece of paper. Now, brainstorm without limits. Write down everything that comes to mind. That's your bucket list. Go back to your list either in the same session or another time and refine it. Set a timeframe (by decade if you like) and prioritise your top three, five and 10 bucket list items. Share the list with a buddy if you like and even designate activities you'd like to do together.

# buy yourself something nice

It's okay to treat yourself now and then. Try tapping into your needs and desires. Sometimes we want to buy something for the quick hit of pleasure that it brings, which is often followed by remorse. But if it's something you've had your eye on for a while and your budget can cope with it, then why not?

# create an 'instead' list

We all know how easy it is to spend 15 minutes scrolling on social media. Create a list of more enjoyable or productive things you could be doing instead. When temptation strikes, go to your instead list and do one of them. #quickwin

# do nothing

'Almost everything will work again if you unplug it for a few minutes, including you.'

ANNE LAMOTT

# take care of small tasks

Small tasks are cumulative in nature. They build up, causing a drain on the brain and unnecessary stress. Don't ignore them. Instead find ways to tackle them effectively. If it takes less than two minutes to complete a task, take care of it right away. Slightly more complicated tasks, or multiple tasks, will need to be addressed differently. Designate a block of time in your weekly calendar when you can do them. Try to batch tasks that can be done together, for example at a single location (your computer perhaps) or on a walk to town.

# edit your to-do list

Have a look at your to-do list. Is it really necessary to do everything on there? Be ruthless and get rid of any non-essential tasks from the list. Next, subdivide the bigger tasks and the smaller ones, and put them in priority order. Then put a plan in place for how and when you are going to deal with them.

# write a meal plan

Deciding what to have for dinner is a drag. Chucking out limp veggies from the fridge is wasteful. Why put yourself through it? It's easy to design a weekly meal plan. You may even want to do it monthly: when you're in the zone, you might as well. Rotating recipes regularly makes the task easier. Designate a day each week to do your planning and your grocery shopping. Cook twice as much as you need and have the leftovers for lunch. That way you only need to plan for one meal a day, plus breakfast and snacks.

# do your daily clean

'Tidying is the act of confronting yourself;
cleaning is the act of confronting nature.'

MARIE KONDO

# throw out the random socks

You could keep a basket of single socks on top of your washing machine waiting for their partners to show up some time. Or, here's a better idea: let them go. If the idea really pains you, then look online for sock reuse ideas – golf-club protectors, hand puppets, bird feeders, that kind of thing.

# do a digital cleanse

Take 15 minutes to do a digital cleanse.
Tackle an overcrowded desktop. File
what needs to be filed and delete the
rest. Be one of those people with a
picture of a mountain or a sunset on
their screen – and that's it. Take the
same ruthless approach to your phone
and other devices. Delete and/or
unsubscribe from apps you don't use.
Get rid of text messages you've been
hanging onto (why?) and back up your
photos and videos. (While you're at it,
make a folder of 10 of your absolute
favourite photos – see #98). You'll free up
storage, potentially save money and feel
heaps better.

# do a quick purge

'Keep only the things that speak to your heart.'

MARIE KONDO

# frame a photo

Digital cameras and smartphones have changed the way we interact with photos. They are now things to scroll through, post on social media and worry about filing. That's all good, but sometimes we forget to do the old-fashioned thing and print out our photos, frame them and hang them on the wall. And look at them. And feel warm and fuzzy. If you have a little more time, you could make an album, perhaps of a family holiday or of your child's first 10 years.

# give yourself a foot rub

'A massage is just like a movie, really relaxing and a total escape, except in a massage you're the star. And you don't miss anything by falling asleep!'

ELIZABETH JANE HOWARD

# do your nails

For some people, doing their nails is a Zen-like experience. It requires concentration and the result is pleasing (hopefully). Through the repetitive motion of nail painting, we hush hush our minds and any potential negative self-talk. Nail painting is a simple gesture that says 'I am worth it'. Unless you are doing something fancy like nail art, it is a small, easily accomplished task that has immediate results.

# go out and take photos

Taking pictures on a digital device is a part of everyday life. It's become a reflex action, done without much thought. Try thinking about it. Take a small number of photos (limit yourself to a number, say three or five). Choose your subject carefully and really look at it before you take the photograph. Taking a photograph attunes us to our environment, improves memory and helps us to focus on positive or meaningful experiences. You chose to photograph something beautiful, right?

# soak up some rays

Sunshine is nature's bubble bath: it's relaxing and it makes you feel good. And it's actually doing you good. Getting out in the sunshine for just 10 minutes a day three times a week will boost your vitamin D levels enough to improve bone health and your immune system. Sun exposure also increases levels of serotonin. Known as the happiness hormone, it does what it says on the tin. The more sunshine in the daytime, the more melatonin you produce at night, helping you have a better night's sleep. If that's not enough, recent studies have made a link between sunshine and weight loss. It seems a few extra rays can reduce body fat and help you shed the kilos.

# walk
# barefoot

'You learn a lot when you're barefoot.
The first thing is every step you take is
different.'

MICHAEL FRANTI

# look up

'Keep looking up...
That's the secret of life...'

SNOOPY

# hygge your bedroom

That word again. Hygge's travelled a long way from its native Denmark to teach us all around the globe how to get cosy in our own special way. There's no space more sacred than your bedroom and cosying it up will increase your enjoyment of it and may improve your sleep too. Invest in bed furnishing that you love. Make your bed every day. Create a reading nook (or zone for your books). Select a few treasured items for your bedside. Consider a humidifier for dry skin and winter snuffles. Put up a nice photo or artwork. Declutter. Destress. And enjoy.

# make your bed

'If you want to change the world,
start off by making your bed.'

WILLIAM H. MCRAVEN

# stay warm

Go the extra mile in winter to make your bedtime the pleasure it should be. Put your pyjamas in the tumble drier for five minutes before putting them on. Put a hot-water bottle in your bed 10 minutes before you turn in. Snuggle in bed with a warm cup of herbal tea, your journal and/or a good book. #sweetdreams

# recap
the day

Before you turn off the light at night,
write down your favourite three things
from the day.

# fuel for self-care

'An empty lantern provides no light.
Self-care is the fuel that allows
your light to shine brightly.'

ANON

# know your power

'You've always had the power my dear, you just had to learn it for yourself.'

GLINDA THE GOOD WITCH (*THE WIZARD OF OZ*)

# know yourself

'Owning your story is the bravest thing you'll ever do.'

BRENÉ BROWN

# love
# yourself

'learning to love yourself is like learning to walk – essential, life-changing, and the only way to stand tall.'

VIRONIKA TUGALEVA

# don't aim for perfection

'Wherever perfectionism is driving us, shame is riding shotgun.'

BRENÉ BROWN

# stay connected

Stick to your regular appointments. If you have meetings with your parents' group, community group or other social group don't let your attendance lapse because you are too busy. If you don't have meetings like this, try setting up a regular coffee date with a friend, or schedule an evening a week to call a friend or family member.

# talk to a friend

'Sometimes talking to your best friend is all the therapy you need.'

ANON

# take screen breaks

Be mindful of your dependency on your phone or social media. If you're struggling to stop scrolling, ask yourself why? What's going on with you?

Put some simple strategies in place to manage it. Turn off your email and work phone outside of work hours. Take an hour screen break, by scheduling 'do not disturb' in the settings on the phone. This will put a stop to messages, calls and notifications for the time you allocate. Try not to have multiple screens open or access to more than one screen. Do one thing at a time, even if it is looking at your phone.

# don't stress

'I stress about stress before there's even stress to stress about. Then I stress over stressing about stress that doesn't need to be stressed about. It's stressful.'

ANON

# be active and eat well

'Today is your day. To start fresh.
To eat right. To train hard. To live
healthy. To be proud.'

BONNIE PFIESTER

# sleep well and laugh loudly

'A good laugh and a long sleep are the two best cures for anything.'

IRISH PROVERB

# cancel plans (if you want to)

'Cancelling plans to read is ok. Skipping a party for the gym is ok. Staying home to cook is ok. Let's encourage it and respect self-improvement.'

JAY SHETTY

# eat a banana split

If you want a banana spilt, eat a banana split. Life is to be enjoyed. Small pleasures are important. Provided you don't only eat banana splits, it will be okay.

# don't focus on being nice

It's not your job to smile at strangers, join in conversations, like posts on social media or agree to participate in things you don't want to do. Remember that.

# let it go

'A soft reminder: not everything that weighs you down is yours to carry.'

ANON

# trust in your body

'In order to trust your body as a guide, the first step is to begin to understand it.'

DEEPAK CHOPRA

'Whenever you feel sad just remember there are billions of cells in your body and all they care about is you.'

ANON

# trust your instincts

'When you are compassionate with yourself, you trust in your soul, which you let guide your life. Your soul knows the geography of your destiny better than you do.'

JOHN O'DONOHUE

# breathe

'Inhale courage. Exhale fear.'

ANON

149

♥

# stay
# disciplined

'You didn't come this far to only come
this far.'

ANON

# keep moving forward

'Don't look back my darling, you're not going that way.'

ANON

# quotes by

**Muhammad Ali**
American professional boxer (one of the greatest of all time), activist and philanthropist.

**Melanie Beattie**
One of America's most beloved self-help authors, whose classic book *Codependent No More* (published in 1996) introduced the world to the term 'codependency'.

**Susan Weiss Berry**
American mindful living and creativity coach.

**Brené Brown**
American author of five No. 1 *New York Times* bestselling books on personal development and courageous leadership: *Rising Strong, Daring Greatly, Braving the Wilderness, The Gifts of Imperfection* and *Dare to Lead.*

**Eleanor Brownn**
American author and blogger, speaker, teacher and entrepreneur who writes regularly about self-care on social media.

**Laurie Buchanan**
American holistic health practitioner, transformational life coach, speaker and author.

**Deepak Chopra**
Indian-born American prolific author, speaker, doctor and world-renowned mind-body healing expert.

**Winston Churchill**
British statesman, army officer, author and twice prime minister of Britain (1940–45, 1951–55).

**LaTisha Cotto**
American life coach, motivational speaker and blogger.

**Mary Davis**
Author, spiritual teacher, artist and mystic entrepreneur.

**Lalah Delia**
Author, spiritual writer and practitioner and wellness educator. Founder of vibratehigherdaily.com.

Ralph Waldo Emerson
American essayist, lecturer, philosopher and poet who led the Transcendentalist movement of the mid-19th century.

Ella Fitzgerald
(aka The First Lady of Song) The most popular female jazz singer in the United States for more than half a century. A recording of the nursery rhyme *A-Tisket, A-Tasket* catapulted her to fame in 1938.

Michael Franti
American rapper, singer-songwriter, poet and activist. Lead singer of Michael Franti & Spearhead.

Sigmund Freud
German-born Austrian neurologist and the founding father of psychoanalysis. Prolific author of books, articles and essays on the subject.

William Ewart Gladstone
British statesman and four-time prime minister of Great Britain (1868–74, 1880–85, 1886, 1892–94).

Glenda the Good Witch
From the screen adaptation (released 1939, starring Judy Garland) of the book *The Wonderful Wizard of Oz* by American author L. Frank Baum.

Dr Sara Gottfried
Harvard-educated American medical doctor turned functional medicine practitioner and author.

Hank Green
American entrepreneur, musician and vlogger known for his YouTube channel VlogBrothers, produced with his brother John Green.

Terri Guillemets
American quotation anthologist at quotegarden.com.

Hafez
Persian spiritual poet and mystic of the 14th century

Nanea Hoffman
American author, creator, social media personality and the founder of the blog Sweatpants & Coffee.

Bell Hooks (Gloria Jean Watkins)
American author and film-maker, academic, feminist and social activist. Author of *aint i a woman?: black women and feminism.*

Elizabeth Jane Howard
Accomplished English novelist, often overshadowed my her marriage to the writer Kingsley Amis.

Rupi Kaur
Indian-born Canadian bestselling author and illustrator of two collections of poetry who also publishes regularly on social media.

**Henry Kissinger**
Controversial German-born American politician and diplomat who served as U.S. secretary of state and national security advisor under Richard Nixon and Gerald Ford.

**Marie Kondo (Konmari)**
Japanese organising consultant and author, bestselling author and media personality.

**Anne Lamott**
American novelist and non-fiction author, known for writing with humour about difficult topics.

**Audre Lorde**
Pioneering African-American feminist, poet, fiction and non-fiction author, librarian and civil rights activist.

**William H. McRaven**
Retired United States Navy admiral and commander of the U.S. Joint Special Operations Command from 2011 to 2014 turned author and public speaker.

**Herman Melville**
American novelist, short-story writer and poet of the American Renaissance period best known for his masterpiece, *Moby Dick*.

**Amy Leigh Mercree**
American author, media personality, holistic health expert and medical intuitive.

**Clark Moustakas**
American psychologist and humanist. Helped establish the Association for Humanistic Psychology and the Journal of Humanistic Psychology.

**Mina Murray**
A fictional character in Bram Stoker's 1897 Gothic horror novel *Dracula*.

**Daniel Nayeri**
Iranian-American chef turned publisher and author of books for young readers.

**John O'Donohue**
Irish poet, philosopher and priest. known for popularising Celtic spirituality.

**Sam Owen**
British relationships and life coach, psychologist, author, blogger, vlogger and media personality.

**Ben Parris**
American journalist and author of science fiction books, educator, museum planner and technology consultant.

**Tom Petty**
American singer-songwriter (the lead singer of Tom Petty and the Heartbreakers), instrumentalist, record producer and actor.

**Bonnie Pfiester**
American fitness trainer and social media motivator.

Robert Putnam
Prominent American political scientist, author and educator, best known for his study of social capital.

Katie Reed
American blogger at It's A Mother Thing, an award-winning blog written by a mum of four boys.

Kellie Rae Roberts
American social worker turned blogger, artist and creative muse.

Virginia Satir
American author, psychotherapist and social worker known for her approach to family reconstruction therapy.

Jay Shetty
English former monk turned internet personality. A host, storyteller, video maker and coach with the mission of 'making wisdom go viral'.

Snoopy
Charlie Brown's pet beagle in the comic strip Peanuts by Charles M. Schulz.

John Steinbeck
Nobel prizewinning American author, known worldwide for novels such as Of Mice and Men and The Grapes of Wrath.

Alexandra Stoddard
American designer, philosopher, speaker and prolific author, an expert on the art of living the good life.

Anna Taylor
American romance writer.

Vironika Tugaleva
Ukrainian-born Canadian artist, life coach, digital nomad and award-winning written and spoken word poet.

Mark Twain
American 19th-century writer, humourist, entrepreneur, publisher and lecturer best known for his novel The Adventures of Huckleberry Finn.

Vincent van Gogh
Dutch post-impressionist painter; one of the most influential figures in the history of Western art.

Brianna Wiest
American journalist, poet and author of books on the topics of wellness and well-being.

Paul T.P. Wong
Canadian clinical psychologist and professor, best known for his work on death acceptance.

Najwa Zebian
Lebanese-Canadian author, poet, inspirational speaker and teacher.